WALKS ALONG THE EAST
JURASSIC COAST

STUDLAND TO PORTLAND

Robert Westwood

A Jurassic Coast Trust Book

Author Robert Westwood
Editor Alison Moss
Design Jonathan Lewis
Production Peter Sills

First Published as *Walking the East Jurassic Coast Portland to Studland* 2010,
this revised edition printed 2018
Jurassic Coast Trust
Mountfield, Rax Lane, Bridport
Dorset DT6 3JP
Tel: 01308 807000
Email: info@jurassiccoast.org
www.jurassiccoast.org

ISBN 978-1-907701-11-5

British Library Cataloguing-in-Publication Data
A catalogue record for this book is available from the British Library.

Any views or opinions expressed in this publication are solely those of the
authors and do not necessarily represent those of the publisher.

In the interests of your personal safety and enjoyment of the World Heritage Site,
the Jurassic Coast Trust recommend that you follow fully all the relevant
safety advice in this book and the Fossil and The Countryside Codes.
The Jurassic Coast Trust can accept no liability whatsoever.

Your purchase supports our work to protect the Jurassic Coast and help anybody and everybody to
love, understand and value it. (Jurassic Coast Trust Registered charity: 1101134) www.jurassiccoast.org

This publication was first published by Coastal Publishing Limited and the Jurassic Coast Trust
is grateful to Peter Sills and Coastal Publishing for their contribution to the World Heritage Site.
This edition has been reprinted by the Jurassic Coast Trust.

Front cover image: Swyre Head and Bat's Head from Durdle Door.

Printed and bound in the United Kingdom.

For guided walks along the Jurassic Coast with the author Robert Westwood see
www.jurassiccoastwalking.co.uk

South West Coast Path
NATIONAL TRAIL

Image Acknowledgements
(Key: t:top, m:middle, b:bottom, l:left, r:right)
Images in this book are copyright of the photographers and artists.

Front cover © Christopher Nicholson / Alamy
All aerial photography and 4t, 9tl, 39t © Coastal Publishing Ltd
Other photography © Robert Westwood except Richard Edmonds: 14b,
57t; Malcolm Turnbull: 19m.

Cross sections © 2000/2013: Dorset County Council, M.R. House and
The Jurassic Coast Trust with most of the Dorset sections based on the
work of House (1993).

The Jurassic Coast Trust and the author have made every reasonable effort to locate, contact and
acknowledge copyright owners and wishes to be informed by any copyright owners who are not
properly identified and acknowledged so that we may make any necessary corrections.

CONTENTS

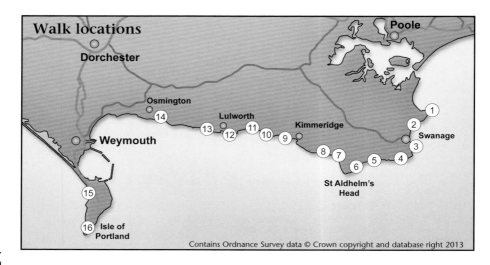

Contains Ordnance Survey data © Crown copyright and database right 2013

The Jurassic Coast has lots to offer the visitor – beautiful scenery, picturesque seaside towns and villages, fine beaches and much of historical interest. All this will delight walkers as they stroll along the excellent coast path. However, these are not the reasons that this stretch of coastline has become a world heritage site; rather it is the record of momentous world events and of the history of life on the planet lying hidden in the cliffs that have led to the designation.

A lovely place to stop for a rest at St. Aldhelm's Head.

The walks in this guide cover the eastern part of the Jurassic Coast from Studland eastwards to Portland. The rocks in this section are of either Jurassic or Cretaceous age. The walks have been chosen to highlight particular aspects of the geology; taken together they outline the story of this part of the Jurassic Coast with, additionally, some interesting snippets of geological information.

The cliffs along the Jurassic Coast are made of rocks from three geological 'periods', the Triassic, Jurassic and Cretaceous. Although the naming of the site might suggest the Jurassic as somehow more interesting or important, this is not so, all three periods fascinate the geologist. The beginning and end of the era defined by these three periods saw globally catastrophic events. Most of life on the planet was wiped out before the Triassic began and again at the end of the Cretaceous. The reasons for these cataclysms are still a matter of debate although there is growing belief that the impact of a giant meteorite together with extensive volcanism were the cause of the extinction that brought about the demise of the dinosaurs and ammonites at the end of the era. Between these events life flowered and flourished, filling the seas with all manner of creatures and the land with wonderful beasts that have captured the popular imagination. Through it all the movement of continents powered by heat deep within the Earth continued to modify the environments; to push up the land, to close some oceans and open up others. In the 95-mile stretch of coastline lies the evidence to unravel this intriguing story; learning a little about it can make a ramble along it so much more interesting.

The majority of the walks in this book are circular. Only one, Walk 2, is one way, but public transport can be used to return to the start point. Walks 3, 4, 10 and 15 are short walks that are suitable for families with young children.

SAFETY FIRST!

Rockfalls and mudslides are an ever-present hazard on this coast and you are most strongly advised to stay away from the base of the cliffs and the cliff top. See page 64 for more information about safety and fossil collecting.

Transport

Public Transport is an excellent way to explore the Jurassic Coast. Poole, Weymouth, Exmouth and Exeter have good rail links to start you on your journey and there are also a range of excellent bus services that serve the towns and villages along the way, including the famous X53, Jurassic Coaster, run by First Bus.

However, bus services change over time and are managed by different operators the length of the coast. We suggest that you check details before starting your journey. Information can be found on the Jurassic Coast Trust website, **www.jurassiccoast.org/travel** but we also recommend that you look at **www.travelinesw.com** or call Travel Line 0871 200 2233.

There are also a number of boat services, either tours or taxi style services at different locations along the coast, why not enquire in your accommodation or TIC as to whether this might add a different dimension to your walk.

Most walks give information about the nearest car park.

INTRODUCTION

OLD HARRY ROCKS

Ballard Down

P

Start/Finish

Walk 1 - Old Harry Rocks

Distance	3.75 miles (6km)
Estimated time	2 hours
...ulty	●●○○○
t	400ft (120m)
	OS Explorer map OL15
g point	SZ 038826

*A very easy walk with quite gentle climbs.
...ful near cliffs and keep dogs on a lead.*

...ne South Beach car park in Studland
...uth past the Bankes Arms pub and
...: at the bottom past the public
...ences. Follow the path all the way
...eadland at Handfast Point. From
...u have a perfect view of Old Harry
...neighbouring sea stacks, as well as
...er Studland Bay and Poole Harbour.
...l Bay was a favourite anchorage
...s in the fifteenth and sixteenth
..., who could not venture through
...w harbour entrance for fear of
...oped.

...th along the cliff edge. Although
you will be turning right along Ballard
Down, ignore the first Purbeck Way
footpath sign and carry on a little way in
order to admire the extensive view over
Swanage Bay, a great spot to sit and eat a
picnic. Continue along the path but at the
next fork keep right to join the Purbeck Way
along Ballard Down. Follow the path along
the top of the down, past a stone seat and
then turn right at a signpost to Studland.
The path goes down towards the village
and joins a road; turn right and follow this
back to the car park.

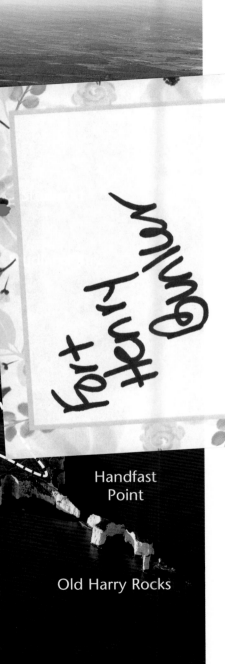

Handfast
Point

Old Harry Rocks

A view over the village of Studland on the path from Ballard Down.

Near the car park is a quaint Norman church. It is worth a visit to see the grave of a remarkable man, Sergeant Lawrence, a veteran of Waterloo. The grave, with details of his career, is near the entrance on the south side.

Studland represents the eastern end of the Jurassic Coast. As you stand on the Chalk ridge to the south of this ancient village and look north over Poole Harbour you are looking at a landscape carved out of soft sands and clays from a different geological era to the one covered in this book.

Chalk is the youngest rock on the Jurassic Coast and was deposited as a calcareous ooze at the bottom of a great sea.

Another period of erosion followed the deposition of the Chalk; southern England was uplifted and much sediment removed back to the sea. This erosion removed any evidence in Dorset and East Devon of the great Cretaceous/Tertiary extinction that wiped out the dinosaurs. Eventually the sea returned, depositing the sands and clays that are typical of the Tertiary rocks of the Hampshire Basin. Some of these rocks were deposited in shallow seas, others formed in rivers and estuaries, the changing geography reflecting continuing Earth movements that were to culminate in the Alpine mountain building episode and which were responsible for some of the structures we see on the Jurassic Coast.

One such structure can be appreciated on our walk. Consider the Chalk ridge which bounds the Isle of Purbeck. The relatively thin width of the ridge indicates that here the Chalk is dipping

Formation of Stacks

Stage 1
An arch forms in the Chalk as the sea works into weaknesses in the rock.

Stage 2
The arch gradually enlarges as more and more Chalk is eaten away.

Stage 3
The arch collapses into the sea, leaving the seaward pillar as an isolated stack.

The Chalk stacks at Handfast Point.

steeply; the original flat layers have been tilted by massive earth movements. On Ballard Down however the ridge broadens, and at Handfast Point the Chalk clearly exhibits near horizontal strata. Walk to the southern side of the ridge and you are back on steeply dipping Chalk. The dividing line is the Ballard Down Fault, a large plane of weakness in the rocks, running parallel to the ridge, where the vertical limb of the giant step fold or monocline has been thrown down to rest up against the horizontal limb. Many such faults are invariably associated with major earth movements and often complicate the geological picture for the interested observer.

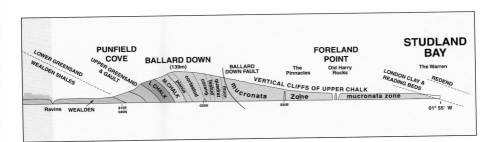

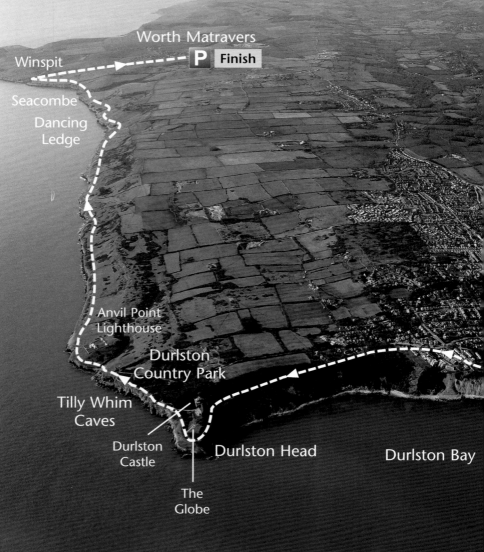

Winspit

Worth Matravers

P Finish

Seacombe

Dancing
Ledge

Anvil Point
Lighthouse

Durlston
Country Park

Tilly Whim
Caves

Durlston
Castle

The
Globe

Durlston Head

Durlston Bay

Swanage

Start

P

Peveril Point

Walk 2 - Swanage to Worth Matravers

Distance	6.9 miles (11km)
Estimated time	4-4½ hours*
Difficulty	●●●●●
Ascent	830ft (250m)
Map	OS Explorer map OL15
Starting point	SZ 029789

*Allows time to explore Dancing Ledge, Seacombe and Winspit

Notes: The Breezer Route 44 bus service runs Monday to Saturday (excluding Public Holidays) between Swanage and Worth Matravers. For timetable information please see www.morebus.co.uk

In Swanage, walk from the bus station to the southern end of the beach near the pier. Follow the coast path through the car park towards Peveril Point. Take the path up the hill alongside Durlston Bay. At the top follow the path to the left to Durlston Country Park.

At Durlston Head go down to the right of the Castle and have a look at the Great Globe. From here follow the coast path westwards past Tilly Whim Caves. Continue past Anvil Point Lighthouse. Where there is a choice of paths take the one nearest the cliff and follow the coastline to Dancing Ledge. Continue on the coast path towards Seacombe. Walk a little way up the valley then follow the coast path, which goes up some steps and continues along the top of the cliffs. Follow the path down to Winspit.

From Winspit follow the path up the valley towards Worth Matravers. Where it meets a wide track on the left keep right and walk up through the field to the village.

WALK 2

PEVERIL POINT

P
Start/Finish

Durlston
Bay

Coastwatch Station

Peveril Point

Plunging syncline
in Purbeck strata

Walk 3 - Peveril Point

Distance	1 mile (1.5 km)
Estimated time	½ hour
Difficulty	●●●●●
Ascent	130ft (40m)
Map	OS Explorer map OL15
Starting point	SZ 035787

Notes: This can easily be combined with Walk 4. Simply follow the coast path from Peveril Point to Durlston Country Park. It is necessary to return the same way.

This is a very short walk for the purpose of exploring the rocks of Durlston Bay, perhaps the best exposure of the Purbeck Beds. Start from the main car park at the southern end of Swanage and follow the road and then path to the Coastwatch Station at the tip of Peveril Point. You can go down to the rocky shore to explore the rocks but take care, the beach is very rough, bouldery and slippery and the cliffs are prone to rockfalls. Dinosaur footprints have been found on some of the exposed bedding planes of rocks that were deposited in coastal lagoons or swamps.

From Peveril Point follow the path along the side of the cliffs towards Durlston Head. At the top of the field there is a seat to admire the view. Then walk down the other side of the field back to the car park.

WALK 3

A limb of a small fold in the Purbeck strata at Peveril Point.

Peveril Point lies at the eastern end of Durlston Bay. The rocks here are limestones and clays from a range of environments both saline and freshwater. Traditionally the Purbeck rocks have been regarded as representing the top of the Jurassic age but they are mostly, if not entirely, from the Cretaceous Period; a reminder that such divisions are based not on rock type but on the fossil evidence within the rocks.

At this point in time the Jurassic seas which spawned the Portland limestones had receded and Dorset enjoyed a warm climate at the edge of the sea. The landscape was characterised by saline lagoons and lush, freshwater swamps. This was the sort of environment where giant dinosaurs roamed; food was abundant and the shallow water would have relieved the pressure on their mighty legs.

A dinosaur footprint in the Purbeck limestone.

How do we know all this? It is a combination of the fossils present and the types of rocks we see. Dinosaur footprints have been found here so this was clearly land. The shelly remains of creatures we see come mainly from species that live in fresh water. Plant remains are found and desiccation cracks are seen, indicating that the shallow lagoon sometimes dried out.

In Durlston Bay the strata dip to the north; at Peveril Point however we see a minor fold within this overall structure. If the tide is out look eastwards from the tip to see two ledges of limestone dipping towards each other. This is a small syncline, shaped like a trough, and represents a small buckle in the strata formed by the same Earth movements that shaped the major structure.

John Mowlem

Swanage is a popular resort that retains the feel of a typical Victorian seaside town. In Victorian times it was a major centre for the export of Purbeck Stone, brought to Swanage from the many quarries and quars (mines) inland. From Swanage it would be rowed out to larger ships anchored in the bay, until a pier was built in 1859. Much of the stone was destined for London, for use in the Victorian renovations of the capital.

A business man who had won several large contracts for the building work was, in fact, a Swanage man. John Mowlem (1788–1868), founder of the well-known construction business, had worked as a stonemason in the local quarries, including Tilly Whim, before moving to London to make his fortune. The boats which took the stone to London for Mowlem's projects could not return empty – they needed ballast to make them safe – so Mowlem filled them with many curiosities from London's streets. These were used to decorate his home town and many can still be seen today.

John Mowlem returned to live in Swanage in 1845 and became a great benefactor to the town. He built the Mowlem Institute for the education and intellectual improvement of the working class, and with his nephew, George Burt, built much of the town's infrastructure; the splendid water tower, now a modern home, can be seen near Durlston Country Park.

DURLSTON

Anvil Point
Lighthouse

Durlston
Country Park

Tilly Whim caves

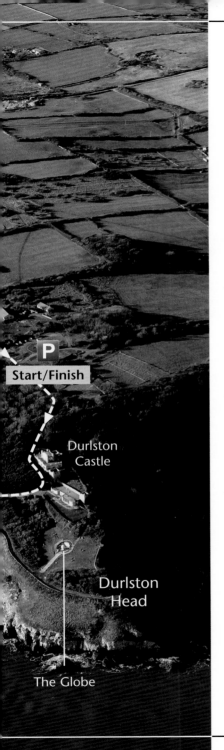

Start/Finish

Durlston
Castle

Durlston
Head

The Globe

Walk 4 - Durlston

Distance	1 mile (1.5km)
Estimated time	1 hour
Difficulty	●●●●●
Ascent	210ft (65m)
Map	OS Explorer map OL15
Starting point	SZ 032773

Notes: A very easy walk with one moderate climb.

There is ample parking space in Durlston Country Park. Join the path that leads to the cliffs passing Durlston Castle and the Great Globe. Follow the coast path westwards along the cliff top. Just past the Tilly Whim Caves (now closed off) there is a small valley showing the remains of quarry workings. Take great care if scrambling about here. Look at the rock face immediately below the caves and you should be able to see the protruding edges of two large ammonites in the horizontal strata.

Continue along the coast path past Anvil Point Lighthouse. Turn on to a tarmac road that leads inland. Go over the small bridge and then take the grassy path to the left up to the top of the ridge. Go right at the top and rejoin the road, which will lead you back to the car park or simply follow the road back to the car park.

Information about the visitor centre, café and other facilities at Durlston Castle can be found on online at www.durlston.co.uk.

WALK 4

Tilly Whim caves, as seen from the coast path below Anvil Point.

After the Kimmeridge Clay had been deposited conditions changed dramatically. Around 150 million years ago only southern Britain was left covered by sea and in these fairly shallow, warm seas the Portland series of rocks were deposited. At first there was much sand and clay, but this decreased and the sediment at the

Two giant ammonites lie on a bedding plane in Portland limestone near Tilly Whim.

bottom became richer and richer in calcium carbonate from the abundance of creatures that used it in their shells and other hard parts. Some calcium carbonate was dissolved in the seawater and later precipitated out, forming a perfect cement for the limestones that were subsequently created. The rolling action of waves across the bottom of the shallow seas encouraged the carbonate to accumulate around tiny grains of sand or shell fragments. These spherical 'ooliths' can just be seen by the naked eye.

The Tilly Whim Caves were quarries that mainly operated in the eighteenth century. During the Napoleonic Wars there was much demand for stone to build fortifications, but after 1815 the demand declined and the quarries were no longer economical. In 1887 the owner of the Durlston estate, Sir George Burt, opened them as a tourist attraction. They were closed in 1976 when rock falls made them unsafe. The stone was cut by skilled workers using hammers and wedges and then lowered by cranes called 'whims' onto barges which transferred them to larger sailing ships offshore.

In the valley to the west of the caves can be seen two giant ammonites, *Titanites*, a zone fossil of the Portland age. They lie horizontal on the bedding plane, exactly in the position they died around 145 million years ago.

Today Durlston Country Park is still a place to see a great variety of wildlife, including wild flowers, butterflies, birds and dolphins. The park's website has a daily diary which keeps visitors up to date on what to see www.durlston.co.uk.

Peregrine falcons can be seen around the cliffs at Durlston.

George Burt

George Burt (1816–1894) was the nephew of John Mowlem, Swanage resident and founder of the great Mowlem construction business. Burt followed his uncle to London to work for him and eventually took over the running of the business in 1845. He, too, was a great benefactor to his native Swanage. It was Burt who bought the land at Durlston with a view to developing it. He built the mock 'castle' and the estate later became a haven for wildlife. The Great Globe at Durlston is one of Burt's creations. It was made from Portland Stone at a stoneyard in Greenwich in 1887. Weighing around 40 tons it was brought to Swanage in fifteen pieces.

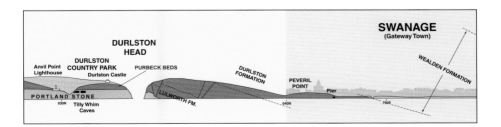

SEACOMBE

Worth
Matravers

Seacombe

Dancing
Ledge

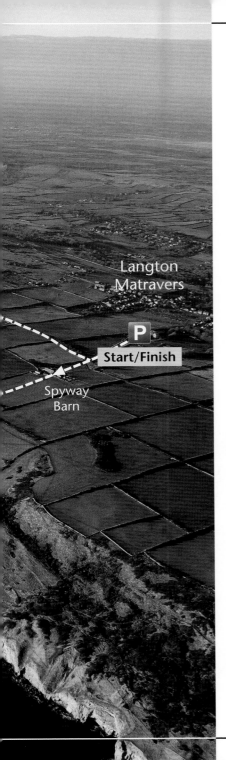

Langton
Matravers

P

Start/Finish

Spyway
Barn

Walk 5 - Seacombe

Distance	4.4 miles (7km)
Estimated time	2½-3 hours
Difficulty	●●●●●
Ascent	700ft (210m)
Map	OS Explorer map OL15
Starting point	SZ 997784

Notes: Take great care if you explore any of the old quarries. One or two moderate climbs. Dancing Ledge is a popular location for rock climbing. A permit for climbing is required from the National Trust.

From the car park at the end of Durnford Drove in the village of Langton Matravers, follow the stony path south to Spyway Barn, owned by The National Trust. Continue past the barn towards the sea. Go over a stile and follow the path downhill signposted 'Dancing Ledge'. It is worth going down to explore Dancing Ledge, an ideal place for those who like to scramble over rocks. It was once the site of extensive quarrying where blocks of Portland Stone were blasted, cut and loaded on to barges waiting offshore.

Follow the coastal path to Seacombe (signposted 1 mile). You will go past small quarries in the cliffs.

Take the path up the valley towards Worth Matravers. After a little while fork left to Worth crossing a footbridge over a stream. (You could carry straight on to join Priest's Way east of Worth but then you would miss the delightful little village and the Square and Compass pub). Go through a gate and walk up the side of the valley: note the

WALK 5

Massively bedded Portland Stone at Seacombe.

medieval strip lynchets. Follow the signs to Worth across another valley. When you reach the village follow the road round to the right and you will come to the Square and Compass, an excellent place for refreshment.

Continue up the road past the pub and you will soon see a footpath on the right with a sign to Swanage (4 miles). Take this and you will shortly meet the wide, stony Priest's Way. You will pass a working quarry in the Purbeck limestones. Turn left onto the path back to the car park just north of Spyway Barn.

Portland Stone was deposited on the floor of a shallow tropical sea. At times when land was relatively distant and little sediment from rivers was polluting

The cliff path on the way to Seacombe with an interesting piece of stone wall!

the seabed, a high concentration of calcium carbonate from shell creatures led to the formation of a wonderful, hard building stone. When conditions remained the same for long periods – hundreds of thousands or even millions of years – the sediment had a chance to form thick, homogeneous layers, increasing its value to the architects and master builders of the future. Such layers were the workplace of quarrymen at Seacombe, Winspit and many other places on the coast of Purbeck.

Calcite or calcium carbonate is not the only mineral used by organisms for hard parts; some, like sponges, use the abundant mineral silica. The remains of these creatures accumulate on the sea floor. They may be dissolved in the seawater, leading to a later precipitation of silica as the concentration of material increases. It is clear that if the rocks we are talking about originated from gradual accretion on an ocean floor, there must have been a process that compacted and hardened them, associated with the ever increasing pressure of sediment above. Geologists call this process diagenesis (from the Greek for 'through' and 'formation') and it is a time when chemical as well as physical changes occur. In some places during the diagenesis of

The cliffs at Dancing Ledge are a favourite practice ground for climbers.

the Portland Stone silica in the form of chert was precipitated out and collected in nodules. There are many layers of these nodules evident in the rocks at Seacombe. The limestone here consists mainly of millions of tiny 'spicules' (like needles) from sponges, originally made of silica. In turn the dissolved silica precipitated out to form the chert nodules.

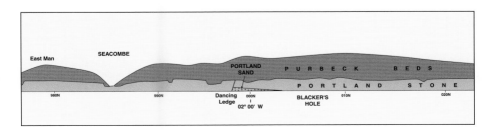

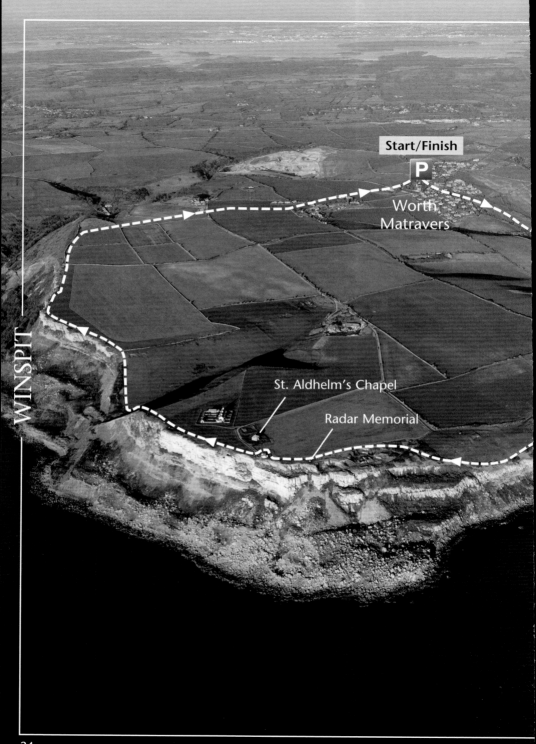

Start/Finish

P

Worth
Matravers

WINSPIT

St. Aldhelm's Chapel

Radar Memorial

Winspit

Walk 6 - Winspit

Distance	4.4 miles (7km)
Estimated time	2½-3 hours
Difficulty	●●●●
Ascent	660ft (200m)
Map	OS Explorer map OL15
Starting point	SY 974776

Notes: One fairly steep climb, which can be avoided by taking the road back to Worth Matravers from the Coastguard Station – but the views along the coast are worth it.

There is an excellent car park on the right as you enter the village of Worth Matravers from the north. From here walk past the Square and Compass pub and you will find the track to Winspit signposted just below the duck pond. It leads south past a row of cottages and then crosses fields to the coast.

At Winspit it is worth exploring the little cove; look out for the giant ammonite Titanites near the water's edge. Take care if you are going to explore the old quarry workings and note the warning signs. Follow the path westwards along the top of the cliff signposted to St Aldhelm's Head.
At St Aldhelm's Head take time to visit the small chapel. Follow the cliff path past the Coastguard Station and round the western side of St Aldhelm's Head. From here there are extensive views along the Jurassic Coast and the dark Kimmeridge Clay which underlies the Portland formations. At one point there is a steep, dry valley to descend and climb. Just after you have passed the cove of Chapman's Pool, take the path to the right to Renscombe; following it across a field

WALK 6

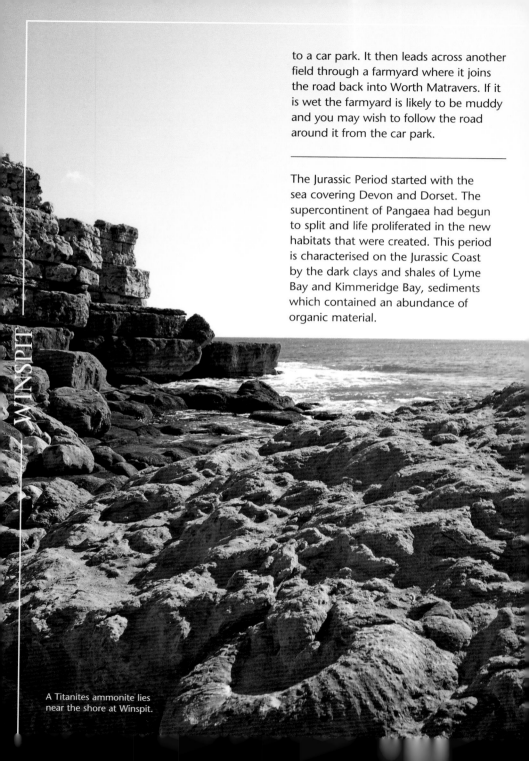

to a car park. It then leads across another field through a farmyard where it joins the road back into Worth Matravers. If it is wet the farmyard is likely to be muddy and you may wish to follow the road around it from the car park.

The Jurassic Period started with the sea covering Devon and Dorset. The supercontinent of Pangaea had begun to split and life proliferated in the new habitats that were created. This period is characterised on the Jurassic Coast by the dark clays and shales of Lyme Bay and Kimmeridge Bay, sediments which contained an abundance of organic material.

A Titanites ammonite lies near the shore at Winspit.

Following the deposition of the Kimmeridge Clay there was a period of uplift and much of Britain was land. Warm, shallow seas persisted over Dorset, however, and the Portland series of rocks were deposited, beginning with the Portland Sand and followed by the famous Portland Stone.

It is tempting to think the divisions of geological time were created on the basis of the rocks. It seems logical to assign a different name when rock type changes dramatically, indicating, as it does, a significant change in the ancient geography (palaeogeography). This is not the case, however; geological divisions are based solely on fossil remains in the rocks. It is life that changes universally with time, a change in environment may be restricted to a certain locality. We can understand this with reference to a fossil, obvious to all, at Winspit. Near the water's edge you can see an example of a huge ammonite from the aptly named *Titanites*. The lifetime of this creature, with others, helps define the age of the Portland Stone; find a specimen and you know what age the rocks are. Other species of ammonite are similarly used to define time zones because, fortuitously, some ammonites evolved quickly into different species each lasting only a relatively short time, geologically speaking.

The Portland Stone on Purbeck shows a variety of different limestones reflecting different environments of deposition including shallow, tropical seas and coastal lagoons. These waters were rich in dissolved calcium carbonate which precipitated out as the sediments were compacted, sometimes forming hard limestones useful for building stone.

St Aldhelm's Chapel
The origins of the chapel at St Aldhelm's Head are somewhat obscure. It is Norman in style and no documentary evidence exists before the thirteenth century. A charming but sad local legend says that it was built by a wealthy nobleman in 1140 after he witnessed his daughter and her husband die in a shipwreck in the treacherous waters off the headland. It would certainly have proved a useful marker in later years. There may have been a chapel here long before the present structure. St Aldhelm became, early in the eighth century, the first Saxon bishop of Sherborne. He was responsible for the building of a number of churches around Dorset and may have built one here. The chapel was restored by Lord Eldon in 1874 and is still used today.

CHAPMAN'S POOL

Kingston

P Start/Finish

Houns-tout

The Golden Bowl

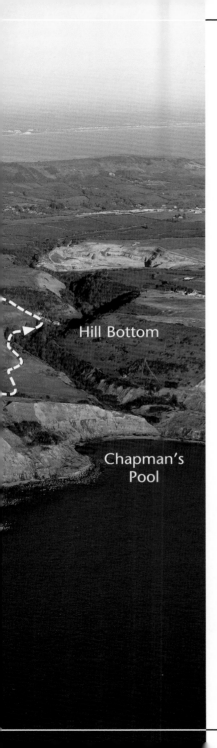

Hill Bottom

Chapman's Pool

Walk 7 - Chapman's Pool

Distance	4.7 miles (7.5km)
Estimated time	2½ - 2¾ hours*
Difficulty	●●●○○
Ascent	560ft (170m)
Map	OS Explorer map OL15
Starting point	SY 954795

Notes: The path down to Chapman's Pool can be very slippery and the path from the cottages at Hill Bottom can be a little overgrown, otherwise this is an easy walk.

In the village of Kingston turn off the through road (B3069) onto West Street. Go past the Scott Arms pub and the church to a car park on the left for Houns-tout Cliff.

Follow the path through the woods signposted 'Houns-tout'. You will soon be out of the woods and onto an open grassy path along the top of the south side of the valley known as the Golden Bowl. Nestling in the valley lies the Encombe Estate; its beautiful house was built by John Pitt in around 1770. He was a distant relative of the famous William Pitt the Younger. It was later sold to John Scott who, as Lord Eldon, was Lord Chancellor under William Pitt. It remained in that family for many years until it was sold in 2002.

The path takes you to the top of Houns-tout from where there are magnificent views along the coast.

From Houns-tout follow the cliff path eastwards down a series of steps that lead

WALK 7

to Chapman's Pool. If you wish there is a path that leads down to the beach. Be careful here as the cliffs are very unstable and the frequent landslides leave the foreshore very slippery. Take the path across the field towards Hill Bottom, through a delightful wooded glade. If you prefer you can take the tarmac road back to Kingston but it is not so interesting.

When you reach the group of cottages at Hill Bottom turn left and follow the path up the hill. This is a little overgrown in places but soon opens out. Go through a gate on the right of way signposted 'permissive path', across the field and you will join the tarmac path back to Kingston and the car park. Take time to see the lovely church built in the 1870s by the third Lord Eldon.

The path from Chapman's Pool leading to Hill Bottom.

Looking at the landslips beneath Hounstout it is not difficult to appreciate how the sea has eroded the soft clays at Chapman's Pool. These are Kimmeridge Clays of the Jurassic, fine sediment that was deposited in a sea relatively poor in

A view over Chapman's Pool from Emmett's Hill.

Westwards from Houns-tout the low cliffs are formed from the softer Kimmeridge Clay.

oxygen. Look at the cliffs either side of Chapman's Pool and you will notice that the Kimmeridge Clay gradually gives way to the Portland Sand and finally the hard Portland Limestone which forms the top of Houns-tout and the headland of St Aldhelm's. The whole sequence records gradually less deep waters culminating in the shallow water limestones at the top of the Jurassic.

The Kimmeridge clays of Chapman's Pool are rich in ammonites and other fossils. These can often be found in the loose shale but be careful not to

linger directly below the cliffs as they are very unstable.

It is easy for the eye to follow the Portland Stone around St Aldhelm's to Houns-tout and across to Swyre Head and thence to the Isle of Portland in the distance. Beneath it the soft clays have been eroded more easily and form less dramatic cliffs, except where they are protected by a cap of the harder limestones. Likewise, inland, higher ground occurs where the limestones provide a protective layer.

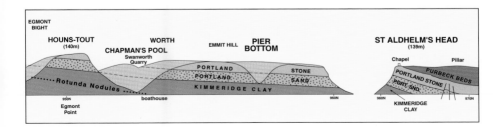

SWYRE HEAD

Start/Finish P

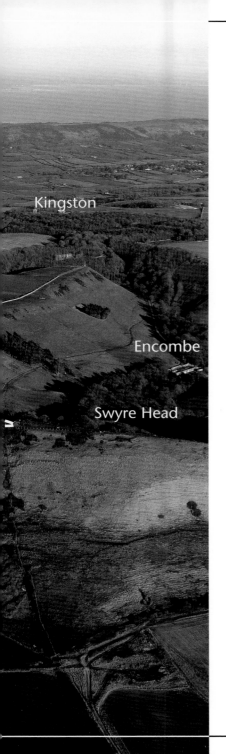

Kingston

Encombe

Swyre Head

Walk 8 - Swyre Head

Distance	1.9 miles (3km)
Estimated time	1 hour
Difficulty	●●●●●
Ascent	260ft (80m)
Map	OS Explorer map OL15
Starting point	SY 943793

Notes: An easy, gentle walk.

In the village of Kingston turn off the through road (B3069) onto West Street. Go past the Scott Arms pub, the church and a car park on the left for Houns-tout Cliff. Continue on to a second, small car park on the left for Swyre Head.

Walk through the stone gates and follow the path up the hill across a field. The path then follows a dry stone wall to Swyre Head. There are stunning views from here, eastwards to St Aldhelm's Head and the Isle of Wight, westwards across Kimmeridge, Gad Cliff and the Isle of Portland. In the valleys to the east and west respectively are the estates of Encombe and Smedmore, each beautifully situated amid fertile farmland.

To return, follow the path by the wall on the west side of Swyre Head. Go through the next field, still keeping by the wall then take a footpath to the right signed 'Kingston'. Follow this back to the car park.

WALK 8

Looking across the 'Golden Bowl' with St. Aldhelm's Head in the distance.

Swyre Head is an excellent place to survey the geology of the Purbecks. Look to the east and you can see St Aldhelm's Head with its horizontal layers of Portland Sand and Portland Stone. You are standing on the Portland Stone, which sweeps round the hillside, almost horizontal. Below you streams have cut valleys into the softer Jurassic strata of the Kimmeridge Clays.

The pattern is repeated to the west where the Portland rocks continue right round to the Isle of Portland. In places in between such as Lulworth and Worbarrow the Portland and Purbeck layers are much narrower and lie steeply inclined; this is the vertical limb of the Purbeck Monocline. It is like a giant step; you are standing on the top,

The view westwards from Swyre Head along the coast. Kimmeridge Bay is nearest, while the steeply dipping Portland and Purbeck beds form the mighty Gad Cliff just beyond.

Kingston Church

The 'new' church at Kingston, built by local craftsmen in the employ of the 3rd Earl Eldon, contains much Purbeck Marble. True marble is the result of the metamorphosis of limestone, heat and pressure 'baking' the rock and making it very hard and durable. This has not happened to the Purbeck Marble, but it is a very hard rock which can be polished like a true marble. It has been used in most of the great cathedrals of southern England. Have a look inside the church if you can and see the marble used in the columns and other details.

The Purbeck Marble is very fossiliferous, the polished sections showing many curved shells. Foremost among these are shells of the snail Viviparus. These creatures

are still alive today; they are molluscs that could tolerate the brackish conditions of the Purbeck lagoons.

horizontal part while to the north the rocks dip steeply down before flattening out again. This, of course, is a very simplified picture; the structure has been complicated by much faulting – lines of weakness where strata have moved relative to one another – the result

of tension in the crust. Nevertheless, standing on this impressive hill, possibly once a headland when the sea level was higher, it is possible to appreciate how the rocks lie in relationship to one another and how this explains some of the features of the coastline.

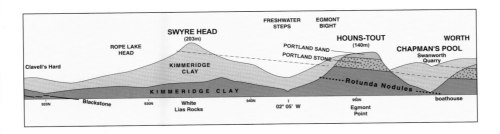

Tyneham Cap

Brandy Bay

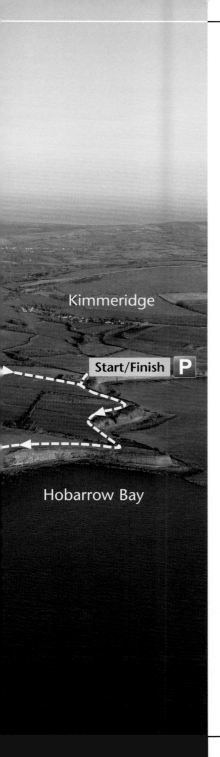

Kimmeridge

Start/Finish **P**

Hobarrow Bay

Walk 9 - Kimmeridge Bay

Distance	3.4 miles (5.5km)
Estimated time	2 hours
Difficulty	●●○○○
Ascent	470ft (140m)
Map	OS Explorer map OL15
Starting point	SY 908791

Notes: Easy but with one fairly steep climb. The walk is on army land, which is only open most weekends and school holidays. For exact opening times call the Lulworth Range Control Office on 01929 404819 or see www.dorsetforyou.com/lulworth-range-walks

From the car park at Kimmeridge Bay take the steps that lead down to the beach but keep right and follow the path up around the cliffs. Soon you will pass through a gate that leads on to the army ranges. Continue to follow the path along the cliffs, keeping between the yellow markers. There are soon lovely views across Hobarrow Bay and Brandy Bay. At the foot of the ridge go over a stile and begin the fairly steep climb up to Tyneham Cap. There is a little bench near the top where you can enjoy spectacular views across Gad Cliff and Kimmeridge Bay. From here you could continue westwards along Gad Cliff for a while to savour another splendid view over Worbarrow Bay and the deserted village of Tyneham. Otherwise head east along the ridge, passing a stone seat which is an excellent place to stop for a picnic.

Continue along the ridge with views across the valley to the north with the Chalk ridge

Clavell Tower on Hen Cliff.

beyond, and across Kimmeridge Bay to the south. At a large sign follow the path almost due south back to the start of the walk.

An alternative walk to do with children is to follow the small gully from the car park down to Kimmeridge beach when the tide is out in order to explore the many rock pools and wander along the ledges. Look in the rubble on the beach for the odd trace of ancient bones; you are likely to find the crushed remains of ammonite shells. Take care when

The path along the ridge north of Kimmeridge Bay.

walking along the slippery ledges and keep away from the base of the cliffs. It is possible to walk round the beach to the Marine Wildlife Centre on the east side, or it can be reached via a path along the top of the cliff. A small footpath leads up Hen Cliff to Clavell's Tower from where there are lovely views across the bay to Gad Cliff.

Kimmeridge has a wonderful succession of rocks deposited in shallow Jurassic seas over 150 million years ago. They are mainly clays, shales and mudstones but also layers of hard limestone which form the hazardous Kimmeridge Ledges. These rocks formed from sediment at the bottom of a Jurassic ocean once teeming with life and are rich in fossils. These sediments have been well researched and it is thought that they were deposited at an average rate (the actual rate varied considerably) of 20-30 centimetres every thousand years. Such an estimate hinges on a very important geological principle; that of uniformitarianism, famously suggested by Charles Lyell in about 1830. Lyell was convinced that the same processes operate today that have done throughout geological history; so by studying present sedimentary environments geologists can interpret what has gone on in the past. When you think that the progressively increasing weight of the sediment has resulted in a squashing by a factor of around 8, it is staggering to think how much was originally laid down. This material came from mountains to the north, Dorset at that time was lying in the Tethys Ocean which had formed when the plate movements caused the supercontinent of Pangaea to break up.

You will notice that the layers of rock at Kimmeridge tend to repeat in the cliffs; this has been interpreted as showing a rhythmical or cyclical sedimentation caused by the environment changing in a rhythmical way. It has been calculated that the cycles lasted around 30,000–40,000 years and it has been suggested that this might coincide with cycles in the tilt of the Earth's axis. This would result in climate belts changing position and hence might explain why the sedimentation changed, resulting in different layers.

Oil well at Kimmeridge.

Kimmeridge has an interesting industrial heritage. The Romans cut and polished the hard, black oil shale, which occurs in the cliffs east of Clavell's Tower, into jewellery. Alum, present in the shale has been used as a fixer in the wool-dyeing industry, and there has even been an attempt to extract lamp oil from the shale. In more modern times Kimmeridge Bay has seen oil being extracted from a small well. The oil lies trapped in Middle Jurassic strata beneath the Kimmeridge Clay; it has nothing to do with the oil shale in the bay. However, the Kimmeridge Clay is the source rock for the huge oil reserves of the North Sea, where it lies deeply buried.

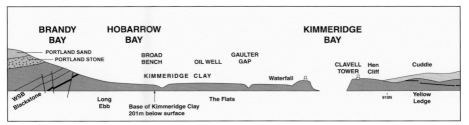

GAD CLIFF

Worbarrow Bay

Gad Cliff

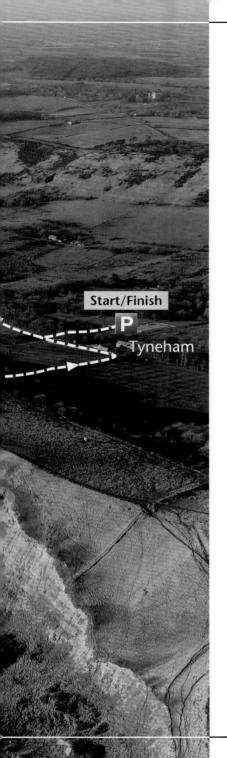

Start/Finish

P

Tyneham

Walk 10 - Gad Cliff

Distance	2-2.5 miles (3-4km)
Estimated time	1-1½ hours
Difficulty	●●○○○
Ascent	360ft (110m)
Map	OS Explorer map OL15
Starting point	SY 882802

Notes: This is a lovely way to see Worbarrow Bay. There are fantastic views along the coast in both directions. It also gives you a chance to explore the beach at Worbarrow. There is a fairly steep climb up to Gad Cliff from Worbarrow Bay – but it is well worth the effort! The walk is on army land, which is only open most weekends and school holidays. For exact opening times call the Lulworth Range Control Office on 01929 404819.

From the car park at Tyneham village take the path along the edge of the wood down to Worbarrow Bay. From here follow the coast path to the left up to Gad Cliff. This cliff forms one of the most spectacular features of the Dorset coastline. Below the cliff is Brandy Bay, which, as the name suggests, was a favourite location for smugglers in the nineteenth century. The base of the cliff is inaccessible by foot and was relatively safe for smugglers to unload their contraband (typically barrels of brandy) to be hauled up the cliff with ropes by accomplices. After about a mile (1.5 km) there is a path on the left down the hill back to Tyneham.

WALK 10

FLOWER'S BARROW

Flower's
Barrow

Worbarrow Bay

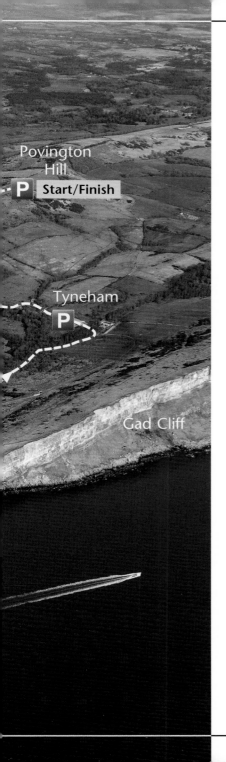

Povington Hill

P Start/Finish

Tyneham

P

Gad Cliff

Walk 11 - Flower's Barrow

Distance	3.4 miles (5.5km)
Estimated time	2½ hours
Difficulty	●●●●●
Ascent	600ft (180m)
Map	OS Explorer map OL15
Starting point	SY 888812

Notes: A straightforward walk with one moderate climb at the end. The walk goes across army land, which is only open most weekends and school holidays. For exact opening times call the Lulworth Range Control Office on 01929 404819. Be sure to build in time to explore the deserted village of Tyneham or see www.dorsetforyou.com/lulworth-range-walks

This is a spectacular walk and ideal for appreciating the structure behind the geology of the Purbecks. Leave the car at Povington Hill car park and after admiring the view take the footpath to the west, which runs beside the road. Follow this path all the way along the Chalk ridge to the Iron Age hillfort of Flower's Barrow. This is one of a number of such fortifications in Dorset and may have been one of those overrun by the Romans in AD43: none have a more dramatic location. The views across Worbarrow Bay are magnificent. Follow the coast path down by the side of the cliffs to the beach. At the southern end of the bay a path leads inland between the remains of old cottages. This was once a favourite spot for smugglers to land contraband. The path leads to the deserted village of Tyneham, requisitioned by the army in 1943 for the preparations for the D-Day landings. It is

WALK 11

Looking across Worbarrow Bay from the Iron Age hillfort of Flower's Barrow.

a charming memorial to a lost way of life; the church and school have been preserved and there is a fascinating display in the latter. To the right of the church as you approach it is a path that leads back up the Chalk ridge (a fairly stiff climb). Follow this and you will rejoin the footpath to the car park.

The Chalk ridge dominates the Isle of Purbeck, running due west from Swanage Bay and cutting the 'island' off from the lowlands to the north. You may be aware that elsewhere, such as on Salisbury Plain, the Chalk covers many square miles of territory, so why, here, is it a relatively narrow ridge? The answer lies in the fact that the chalk layers are dipping steeply; the ridge is simply the edge sticking up. When we see a particular rock type covering large areas it is because

the layers generally lie flat; when we see rocks on the surface in quite thin bands it is usually because we are seeing just the edges of strata that have been tilted or folded. During the Alpine mountain building episode the older strata of Dorset were subject to earth movements and were folded into a giant step-fold or monocline. The Chalk now dips to the north; imagine it rising out from the ridge and gradually becoming horizontal as it goes out to sea, above the Jurassic layers which follow the same pattern.

At the other end of Worbarrow Bay the Jurassic Portland and Purbeck strata are doing the same: they are older and therefore underneath the Chalk. Sandwiched between them are the softer Cretaceous rocks of the Wealden Series which form the valley. These are much more easily eroded than the

Chalk or the hard Portland Stone and so form the vale which runs the length of the Isle of Purbeck and accounts for the shape of Lulworth Cove, Worbarrow Bay and Swanage Bay.

These softer rocks have been much studied and it is clear that they formed in a variety of environments; some were deposited in the estuaries and deltas of big rivers while others were formed in shallow seas. This, too, is an indication of the effect of global tectonics and the movement of plates resulting in changes of sea level. The concept of sea level changes can sometimes lead to confusion. We know that climate change can alter the level of the sea globally: ice ages at times lowered the sea level considerably as a huge quantity of water was trapped on land in the form of glaciers. When this melted the sea level rose again. However, when we talk of the sea invading the land during the early Jurassic and then retreating again, we are talking about tectonic events. It is the giant earth movements associated with plate tectonics that have caused landmasses to be uplifted and oceans squashed out of existence. Thus when we talk about layers of sediments that originated in different environments, it is a reflection of the movement of the giant plates of the Earth's crust.

Tyneham village

The deserted village of Tyneham is a place that raises mixed emotions. There is undoubted sadness that this lively, picturesque settlement was requisitioned by the army in 1943 during training for the D-day landings. The inhabitants were relocated just before Christmas and promised that one day they would be allowed to return. This never happened and Tyneham remains part of the army training ground. However, Tyneham is now a beautiful, secluded and totally un-commercialised site that delights summer visitors with its scenery and wildlife. It has to be said that the army maintains it extremely well, and as a result Tyneham stands as a moving tribute to a lost, rural way of life.

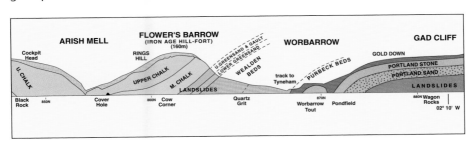

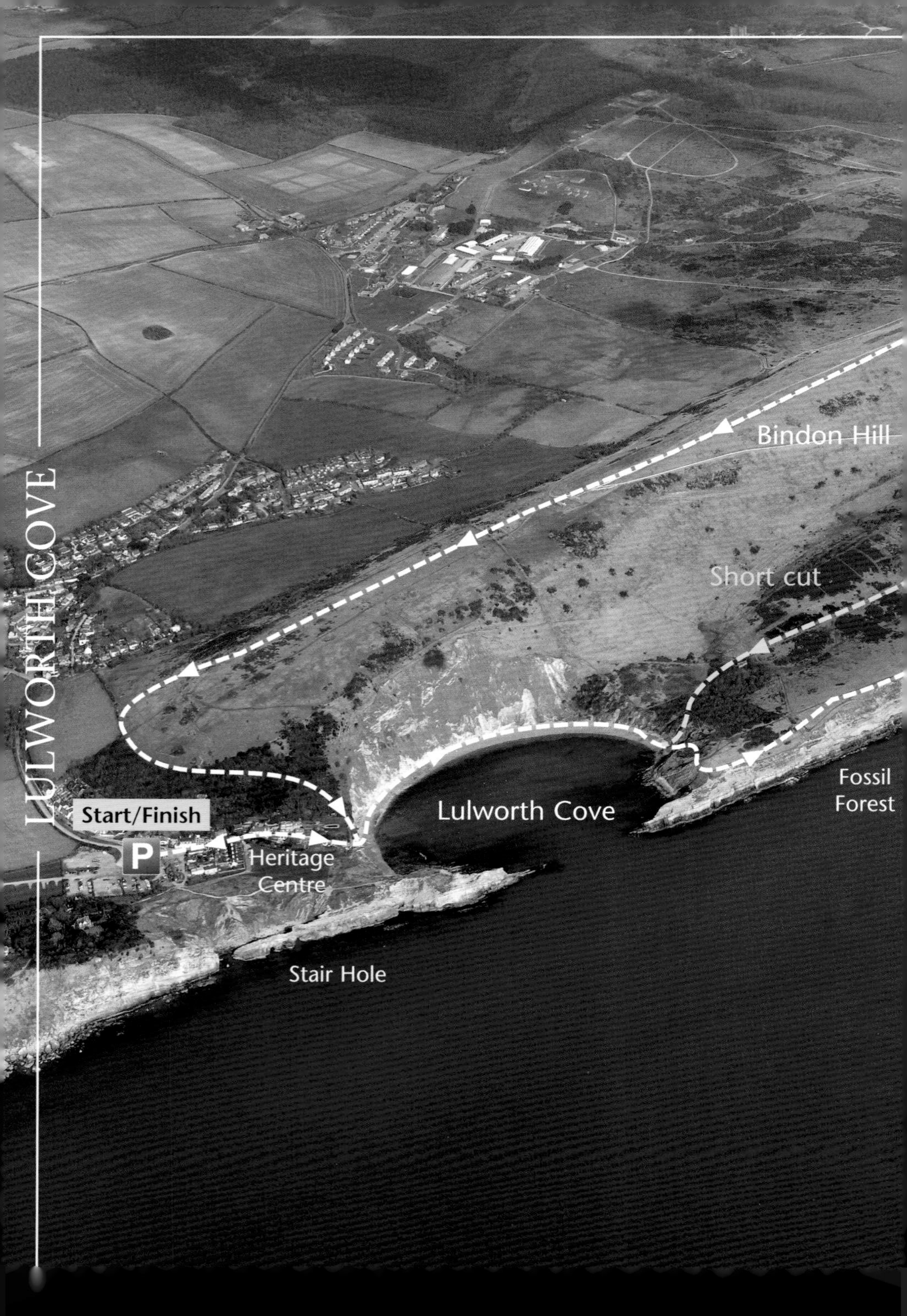

LULWORTH COVE

Bindon Hill

Short cut

Lulworth Cove

Fossil Forest

Start/Finish

P

Heritage Centre

Stair Hole

Mupe Bay

Walk 12 - Lulworth Cove

Distance	4.7 miles (7.5km)
Estimated time	3 hours
Difficulty	●●●●●
Ascent	500ft (150m)
Map	OS Explorer map OL15
Starting point	SY 822800

Notes: Walking around the beach depends on the tide (check the tide times before setting off); if necessary take the path up and around the cliffs. The climb up Bindon Hill is steep. This walk crosses army firing ranges which are only open most weekends and during the school holidays. For exact opening times call the Lulworth Range Control Office on 01929 404819 or see www.dorsetforyou.com/lulworth-range-walks

The walk begins where the road leads on to the beach at the end of the B3070. You can park at the Heritage Centre. Walk around the beach to the far end of the cove. There is a path up to the top of the cliff. After admiring the views of the cove head eastwards along the path closest to the sea. Follow it to a gate where you will be entering the firing range. From here on you will be walking between yellow markers that indicate the path. Continue eastwards to Mupe Bay, although you may first want to follow the path down towards the sea that leads to the Fossil Forest. This is well worth a visit, but it can also be seen from the main path. At Mupe Bay there is a path down to the lovely, secluded beach – an excellent place to stop for lunch.

Keep following the yellow markers and you will soon be faced with a choice. If you

WALK 12

Lulworth Cove, where the steeply dipping, resistant Portland and Purbeck beds form the entrance to the bay.

don't want to do the steep climb up Bindon Hill take the lower path to the left which will take you back to Lulworth Cove. Otherwise keep right and follow the path up the hill, signposted 'Coast Path to Kimmeridge'. At a gentle pace and stopping to admire the view now and again, it will take about half an hour to reach the top. From here you can see Lulworth Castle to the north and the whole of Poole Harbour.

Before heading westwards on the path back to Lulworth it is worth a short walk in the opposite direction (about 20 minutes there and back) to look over Arish Mell and Worbarrow Bay. The views north from this path continue to be impressive but are somewhat spoilt by the dilapidated military hardware left on the firing ranges. Follow the path along the ridge back to Lulworth. You will reach a footpath that leads down to the road leading to the cove. Follow the road down to the car park. If you

wish the walk can be done in the other direction, avoiding the steep climb up Bindon Hill.

The oldest rocks at Lulworth are the Portland and Purbeck strata, typically limestones that have formed at the bottom of shallow, tropical seas or freshwater lagoons. They contain much material from ancient creatures with carbonate shells and are often rich in fossils. These rocks form the "gateway" to the cove and are quite hard and resistant. A popular explanation of the shape of the cove is that once the sea broke through these strata it quickly eroded away the softer, younger sands and clays which comprise the Wealden beds. Hence the hollowed out, circular appearance of the cove. However, it seems more likely that the limestones were breached by a river formed from the confluence of two streams flowing down the valleys either side of the cove (the eastern side is now a dry valley). These streams would have had considerable erosional power towards the end of the ice age when sea levels were lower. Thus Lulworth Cove may be a partially submerged river valley or ria.

Rocks which form on the sea floor do so in horizontal layers; look at the Portland and Purbeck strata at the entrance to the cove and you will see that the layers are tilted steeply to the north. The other rocks are too, although this is more difficult to recognise. They have all been bent into a huge fold by enormous forces generated as plates of the Earth's crust collided. This was part of the Alpine mountain building episode 15–20 million years ago as the African plate moved northwards to collide with the Eurasian plate. Compared to the intense deformations, which pushed up

the mountains and carried huge slices of the Earth's crust many kilometres northwards, the folding along the Jurassic Coast represents peripheral ripples transmitted, perhaps, through older, underlying 'basement' rocks. Stand at the beginning of the walk and imagine the Chalk carrying on up and over the Portland and Purbeck strata and then dipping gently southwards out to sea.

The Fossil Forest is one of the gems of the Jurassic Coast. Access is difficult, but if it is open you can see the preserved remains of trees (typically of Juniper or Cypress type) and of algal growths that formed around the stumps of rotting trees (stromatolites) about 140 million years ago. The trees may have been killed by the rapid advance of a salty lake, which helped preserve them.

Stair Hole

Here the sea has breached the limestones and is beginning to widen out a bay behind. On the eastern side of Stair Hole is the famous Lulworth Crumple, minor but fairly complex folds in the thin Purbeck beds. These folds are the result of compression

during huge earth movements in the Tertiary era; the same earth movements that led to the formation of the Alps. These folds are like minor ripples in the much larger Purbeck Monocline, of which the steeply dipping strata at Lulworth are one limb.

You might think that if you applied sufficient compression to rocks like the Purbeck and Portland limestones they would shatter rather than bend into graceful folds. Imagine, though, the strata deeply buried, heated somewhat and compression applied very gradually. Perhaps then we can appreciate that the rocks might behave in a more fluid manner.

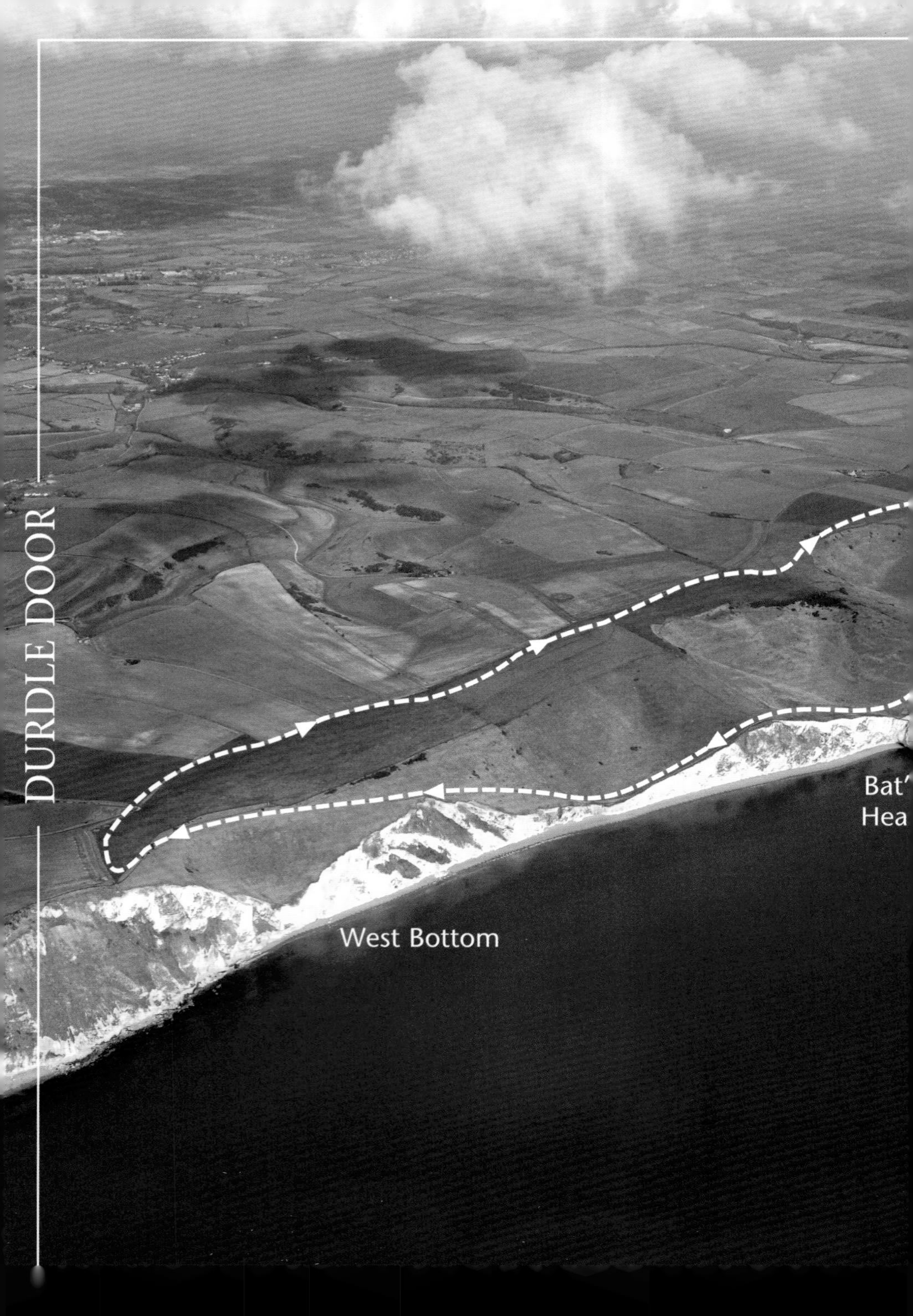

DURDLE DOOR

West Bottom

Bat'
Hea

Newland's Farm

Start/Finish

P

Holiday
park

Swyre Head

Durdle
Door

Walk 13 - Durdle Door

Distance	4.7 miles (7.5km)
Estimated time	2½-3 hours
Difficulty	•••••
Ascent	700ft (210m)
Map	OS Explorer map OL15
Starting point	SY 811804

Notes: An easy-to-follow route but some steep climbs. The path goes very near the cliff edge at times; take great care.

There is a large car park near the coast at Durdle Door Holiday Park. If that is closed it is usually possible to park just outside the gates or on the road leading up to them.

The walk starts on the coast path above Durdle Door. Follow the track that leads down into Scratchy Bottom and then steeply up Swyre Head. The coast path from here is like a roller coaster, first down into a valley and then steeply up again. From the narrow promontory of Bat's Head there are spectacular views along the chalk coast, although it is difficult to pick any one place along this stretch of coast as having the 'best' views. At West Bottom the path verges a little away from the sea and passes by a Beacon, a tall, narrow, stone pyramid. Follow the path around the hillside and then turn right and inland along a path to Daggers Gate. Keep to the left of the field and follow the path back along the ridge, keeping the fence on the left. Near the end, as you approach Durdle Door, take the path to Newland's Farm; keep to the left of the dry valley (Scratchy Bottom) and walk past the farm to the Holiday park.

WALK 13

Late on in the Cretaceous Period, just over 100 million years ago, conditions in southern England changed dramatically. A warm, shallow sea became widespread, resulting in the deposition of the Chalk, a rock that has become a symbol of southern England for thousands returning to these shores by ship or boat.

Chalk is the youngest of the rocks of the Jurassic Coast and, with the preceding Cretaceous rocks, overlies the Jurassic rocks unconformably. The Jurassic strata were raised above sea level and eroded before the sea returned and marine deposition resumed. In the west of the Jurassic Coast all the Jurassic rocks were removed and the Cretaceous lies on top of much older Triassic strata.

It is easy to understand the symbolism attached to this unique rock, which, in its purest form, is brilliant white. The sheer, dramatic cliffs have offered

Looking westwards along the coast from the Chalk promontory of Bat's Head.

Chalk cliffs viewed from the beach at Durdle Door.

forbidding protection from invaders, and now provide a welcome for natives and visitors. Outcropping from Dorset to the Yorkshire coast, it forms a familiar landscape in the English countryside.

The oldest layers in the Chalk contain quite substantial amounts of terrigenous material – sand and clay that has been eroded from land and dropped in the sea by rivers. In newer layers the amount of such material diminishes and we see almost 'pure' chalk. Consider what this means: as you look at the Chalk cliffs, hundreds of feet high, there is little coarse sediment in them – so how were they formed? We now know that it was the gradual accumulation of the hard parts of tiny organisms, almost entirely coccoliths. Coccoliths are tiny plates of calcite formed by coccolithophores, single-celled algae. They live in vast numbers throughout the upper regions of the oceans.

Chalk, then, was formed in a sea where there was very little sediment derived from nearby land. Some have speculated that the Chalk seas were surrounded by waterless deserts. Imagine how long it must take for microscopic skeletal parts to collect at the bottom of an ocean and be compressed and hardened to form

Goats enjoy a precarious view of Durdle Door from Swyre Head.

layers hundreds of feet thick. The wonder does not stop there; each tiny coccolith is like a snowflake, wonderfully intricate and beautiful, shaped like a hubcap and only about three one-thousandths of a millimetre in diameter! The coccoliths are used by the organisms for protection; each one surrounds itself with 20 or 30 of the plates. Used ones are discarded and scientists estimate that coccolithophores are dumping around 1.5 million tons of calcite a year in the world's oceans (source NASA Earth observatory).

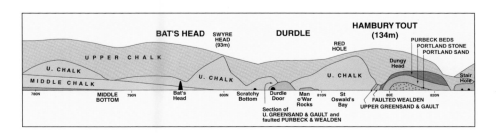

Osmington Mills

P Start/Finish

Spring
Bottom

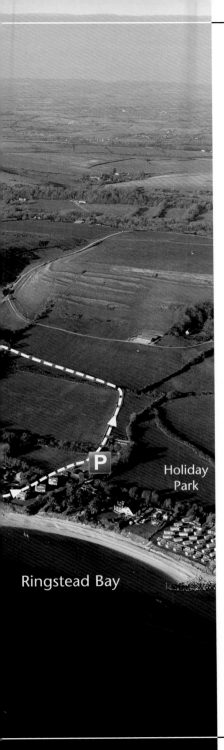

Ringstead Bay

P

Holiday
Park

Walk 14 - Osmington Mills

Distance	3.1 miles (5km)
Estimated time	1½ hours
Difficulty	●●●●●
Ascent	130ft (40m)
Map	OS Explorer map OL15
Starting point	SY 736817

Notes: A very easy and straightforward walk, but you may want to begin at Ringstead Bay.

Park carefully along Mills Road near the Smuggler's Inn in Osmington Mills. There is also a large car park at Ringstead Bay and you may prefer to start and finish the walk from here. Of course it is also possible to make use of the Smugglers' Inn before or after the walk!

Start the walk by going round the back of the pub and joining the coast path to Ringstead Bay. This is easy to follow and at Ringstead follow the tarmac road past the car park. Continue on the road for a little while, round the bend to the left and just before a white house turn left on a path into woodland. Continue on the path through the woodland, following signs to Osmington Mills, not the coast path. You will go uphill past a thatched cottage and then along a small road back into Osmington Mills.

By the holiday chalets you need to take a small path on the left by a fence. You will come out at a holiday park from where you can follow the road a short distance back to the start point.

WALK 14

The shore at Osmington Mills showing steeply dipping layers of Jurassic limestone.

Upper Jurassic rocks are splendidly displayed at Osmington Mills, and provide us with much information about conditions 150 million years ago.

The oldest strata we see are clays formed in much the same environment as the Lias deposits seen around Lyme Regis. Following the deposition of these clays conditions changed somewhat, leading to the formation of oolitic limestones (see walks on Seacombe and Portland), which form in shallow, high-energy environments where there is much dissolved calcium carbonate derived from the hard parts of marine animals. Such limestones from the Osmington Oolite Series can be seen particularly well at low tide on the beach, the bedding planes inclined very steeply. Below these limestones and therefore predating them are rocks known as grits. These have a large content of relatively coarse sandy material derived from nearby land and brought to the sea by rivers. These can be seen east of the small slipway. Look out for cross-bedding, another indicator of a high-energy environment at the time of deposition.

At Ringstead Bay we see the Kimmeridge Clay again. To the east of the bay the geology is complicated by much faulting and in the mighty cliffs of White Nothe we see the Chalk dipping south and lying unconformably on the Kimmeridge Clay. This indicates a break in sedimentation when a period of uplift and subsequent erosion removed older strata before the sea returned.

The walk takes us through woodland past the aptly named Spring Bottom. The hills around here are of the Chalk and springs emerge where the permeable Chalk rests on impermeable clays. Tracing the spring line is one of the ways geologists map the surface outcrop of strata.

Trace fossils

Fossils come in all shapes and sizes. Not all are the actual remains, moulds or casts of living organisms. Some fossils are the traces of an animal in the sediment that was once its habitat. The image on the right reveals a worm burrow about 30cm long, showing faint U-shaped traces made as the animal moved up and down in the sediment. Dinosaur footprints are an obvious example of these 'trace fossils' but more common are the tracks of creatures which crawled over or burrowed in the soft sediment at the bottom of ancient oceans. Trace fossils can be really useful indicators of ancient environments. Some worm species, for example, only live in very shallow seas.

Osmington Mills is a good place to find trace fossils. Examine the bedding surface of the rocks for casts of worm burrows or you might see them in cross-section if you look at the strata from the side. Other creatures such as bi-valves burrowed in the soft

sand and clay and the traces of these can also sometimes be seen. Naturally, identifying an animal from its tracks and burrows can be rather more difficult than from conventional fossils, but geologists are helped in this by the traces of animals that occupy such environments today. It is still fun for the amateur to be able to find the petrified burrows of worms and shellfish that lived on the ocean bottom 80–90 million years ago.

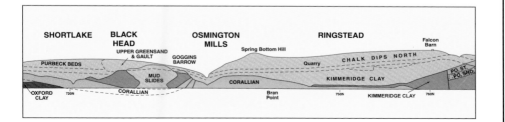

SHORTLAKE   BLACK HEAD   OSMINGTON MILLS   RINGSTEAD   Falcon Barn

UPPER GREENSAND & GAULT   GOGGINS BARROW   Spring Bottom Hill   CHALK DIPS NORTH

PURBECK BEDS   Quarry   PO. ST. PO. SND.

MUD SLIDES   CORALLIAN   KIMMERIDGE CLAY

OXFORD CLAY   720N   CORALLIAN   Bran Point   750N   KIMMERIDGE CLAY   760N

TOUT QUARRY

Start/Finish

P

Whim or
crane

Tout Quarry

Walk 15 - Tout Quarry

Distance	1½-2 miles (2-3km)
Estimated time	As long as you like
Difficulty	●○○○○
Ascent	N/A
Map	OS Explorer map OL15
Starting point	SY 689731

Notes: Tout Quarry was a commercial enterprise for over 200 years, between 1780 and 1982. Today its labyrinth of alleyways, tunnels and quarry faces is being put to creative use. The Portland Sculpture and Quarry Trust maintain a fascinating sculpture park, with over 70 sculptures, large and small, on display around the quarry.

As you leave Fortuneswell on the A354 heading south there is car parking at the top of the steep section on the left in front of the Heights Hotel. There are wonderful views from here over Weymouth and Chesil Beach. You will need to cross the main road carefully as you head for the old 'whim' (crane) that you passed by the side of the road. A grassy path from here leads to Tout Quarry. There is no need to follow a specific route; take time to wander round the quarry to view the sculptures, but don't forget to include the coast path on the western side of the quarry where there are again spectacular views. The tall cliffs show the layers of Portland Stone sloping gently southwards to the sea. Here at the northern end of the Isle of Portland, the underlying Kimmeridge Clay is revealed by this southerly dip.

WALK 15

PORTLAND BILL

Southwell

P

Information
Centre

Pulpit Rock

Portland
Bill

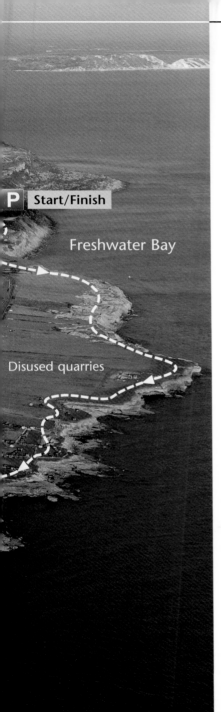

P **Start/Finish**

Freshwater Bay

Disused quarries

Walk 16 - Portland Bill

Distance	4 miles (6.5km)
Estimated time	2½ hours
Difficulty	●○○○○
Ascent	165ft (50m)
Map	OS Explorer map OL15
Starting point	SY 693704

Notes: An easy level walk.

From the car park at Cheyne Weare follow the coast path south towards Portland Bill. You will have to follow the road for a short while before branching off on a track to the left marked 'coast path'. Follow this all the way to Portland Bill, past a number of old quarry sites on the cliffs.

After exploring Portland Bill go round the lighthouse and follow the coast path to the west. Go across the grassy area next to the MoD buildings and then take the path that follows the coast. At a stone marker just before the large buildings take the path to the right signed 'East Cliff'. Follow this path, keeping left when it appears to split (follow the footpath signs). You will reach a road where you should bear right and then right again after a short while. At the Eight Kings pub turn left at the mini-roundabout and follow the road back to the starting point.

WALK 16

Old quarry workings at Portland Bill.

The Isle of Portland is the classic location to see the Portland Stone. It is an 'oolitic' limestone, formed from millions of tiny spherical ooliths, created as layers of calcium carbonate grew around grains of sand or shell fragments, prompted by the rolling motion of waves and currents in a shallow, tropical sea.

A disused quarry on the east coast of Portland showing massively bedded Portland Stone.

The layers would have formed as horizontal sheets on the sea floor, gradually accumulating over millions of years. As you walk past the limestone cliffs and the old quarry workings notice the varying thicknesses of the layers. The limestone layers of the Portland Stone, often over a metre thick, indicate relatively long periods of settled conditions. It is difficult to estimate the rate at which the sediment formed but may be in the order of 50-100 centimetres every thousand years.

Two raised beaches around Portland Bill indicate higher sea levels during the warm periods of the last Ice Age. The western beach, largely contained within the fenced off area, is around 240,000 years old while the eastern beach, running along the low cliff edge by the lighthouse and café, is about 125,000 years old. The beaches can be seen as masses of rounded pebbles lying on a shattered surface of the hard limestone rock.

The Portland Stone was deposited in a high-energy environment. That is to say there were strong currents rolling the sediment on the seabed backwards and forwards. One indication of this is the 'cross-bedding' that can sometimes be seen in the rocks. This appears as faint inclined layers cutting across other inclined layers, rather like the structure found in sand dunes. This is indicative of formation in a very shallow sea where the surface tidal movements extended down to the sea floor.

Oyster Beds

Near Pulpit Rock on Portland Bill you will see another indication of a very shallow sea. Oyster shells are very common in the rocks here. These molluscs are still around today and we know that they live, cemented to the bottom, in very shallow waters offshore or in estuaries.

Another view, looking northwards, along the east coast of Portland.

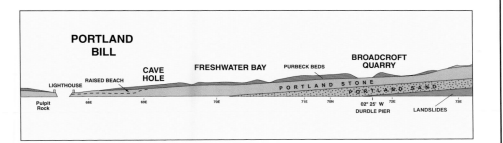

SAFETY
On the beach and coast path

- Stay away from the base of the cliffs and the cliff top and ensure that children and dogs are kept under control.
- Do not climb the cliffs. Rockfalls can happen at any time.
- Beware of mudslides, especially during or after wet weather.
- Always aim to be on the beaches on a falling tide and beware of the incoming tide, especially around headlands. Be sure to check the tide tables.
- Beware of large waves in rough weather, especially on steeply shelving beaches.
- Observe all permanent and temporary warning signs; they advise on hazards and dangers. Check routes beforehand by visiting www.southwestcoastpath.com
- Be very careful on rocky foreshores which often have slippery boulders.
- Stay within your fitness level – some stretches of coast can be strenuous and/or remote.
- Make sure you have the right equipment for the conditions, such as good boots, waterproof clothing and sun screen if appropriate.
- Follow The Countryside Code.

Emergencies

In an emergency dial 999 or 112 and ask for the Coastguard, but be aware that mobile phone coverage in some areas is very limited.

FOSSILS
Collecting fossils

- The best, and safest place to look for fossils is on the beach, away from the base of the cliffs, where the sea has washed away soft clay and mud.
- Do not collect from or hammer into the cliffs, fossil features or rocky ledges.
- Keep collecting to a minimum. Avoid removing in situ fossils, rocks or minerals.
- The collection of specimens should be restricted to those places where there are plenty of fossils.
- Only collect what you need... leave something for others.
- Never collect from walls or buildings. Take care not to undermine fences, bridges or other structures.
- Be considerate and don't leave a site in an unsightly or dangerous condition.
- Do not use a hammer on flint or chert, which shatter into sharp fragments.
- Some landowners do not wish people to collect – please observe notices.

The West Dorset Fossil Collecting Code of Conduct

- This applies between Lyme Regis and Burton Bradstock.
- Collectors are asked NOT to dig in the cliffs without permission.
- Important fossil finds should be registered at the Charmouth Heritage Coast Centre.
- The full code is available from Charmouth Heritage Coast Centre or by logging onto www.charmouth.org/chcc

The Jurassic Coast Trust is the organisation that proudly has the responsibility for looking after England's only natural World Heritage Site, the Jurassic Coast. The Trust is a small charity with a huge remit and big ambitions for the Dorset and East Devon Coast, and we would love you to get involved. Go to **jurassiccoast.org/inspired** for more details.

The South West Coast Path covers 630 miles from Minehead to Poole, this National Trail leads you through diverse landscapes, all with their own unique story to tell. To find out more about the longest and most popular of the UK's 15 national trails, and the South West Coast Path Association, visit **www.southwestcoastpath.org.uk**